Number One Hit[s]
for Keyboard

Music arranged and processed by Barnes Music Engraving Ltd.,
East Sussex TN22 4HA, UK.

Published 1994

**International
MUSIC
Publications**

International Music Publications Limited
Griffin House 161 Hammersmith Road London W6 8BS England

All I Have To Do Is Dream

Words & Music by Boudleaux Bryant

Suggested Registration: Electric Piano
Rhythm: Soft Rock
Tempo: ♩ = 92

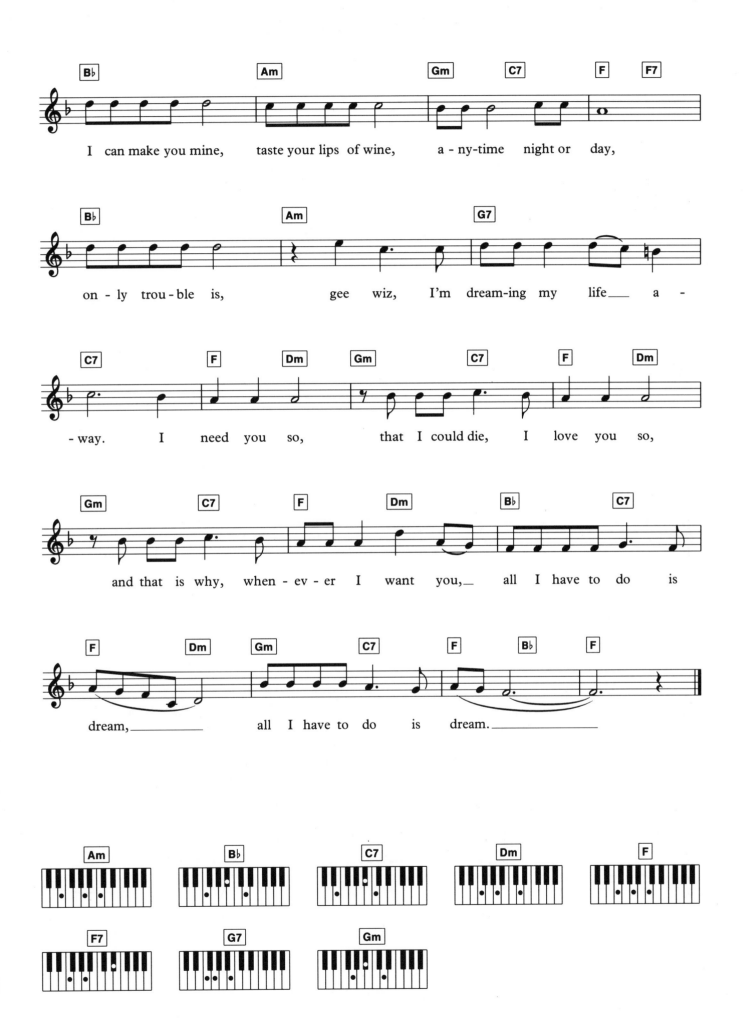

AMAZING GRACE

Traditional

Suggested Registration: Flute
Rhythm: Waltz
Tempo: ♩ = 86

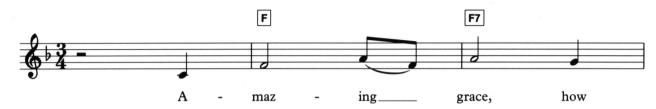

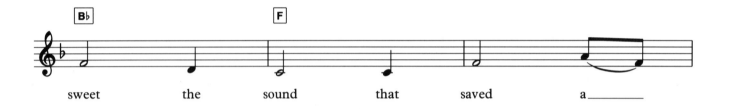

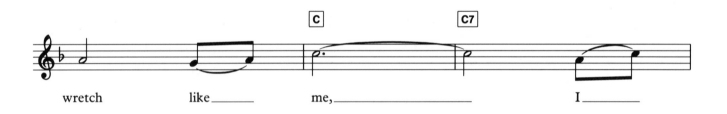

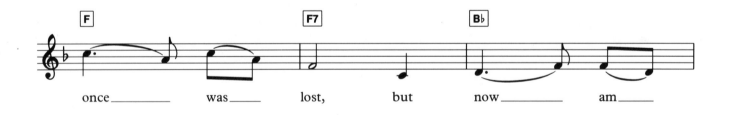

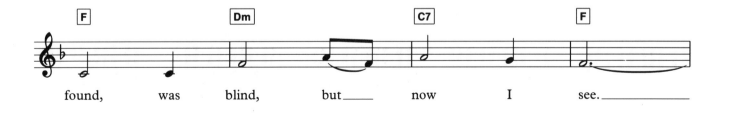

'Twas grace that taught my heart to

fear, and grace my fears re - lieved,

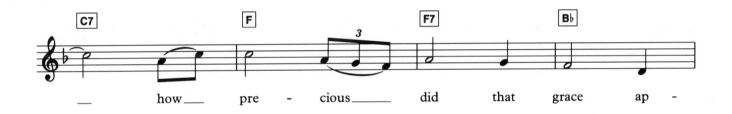

how pre - cious did that grace ap -

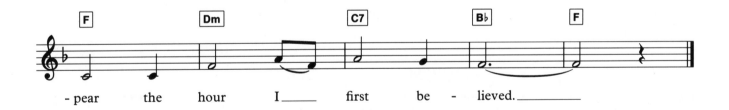

- pear the hour I first be - lieved.

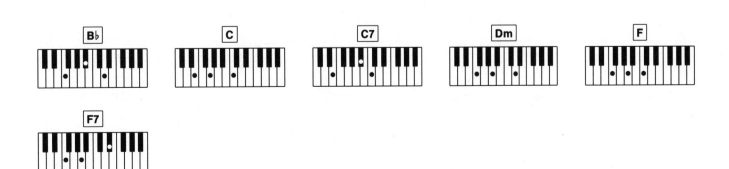

ANNIE'S SONG

Words & Music by John Denver

Suggested Registration: Pan Pipes
Rhythm: Waltz
Tempo: ♩ = 140

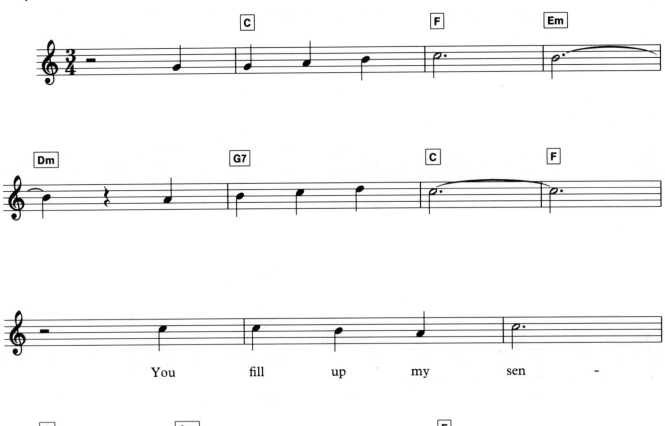

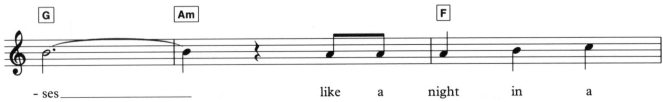

You fill up my sen -

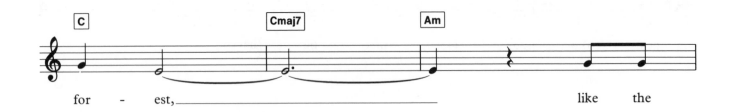

- ses _____ like a night in a

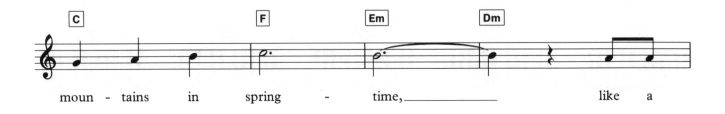

for - est, _____ like the

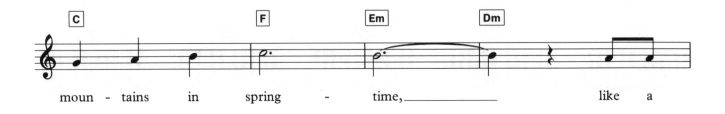

moun - tains in spring - time, _____ like a

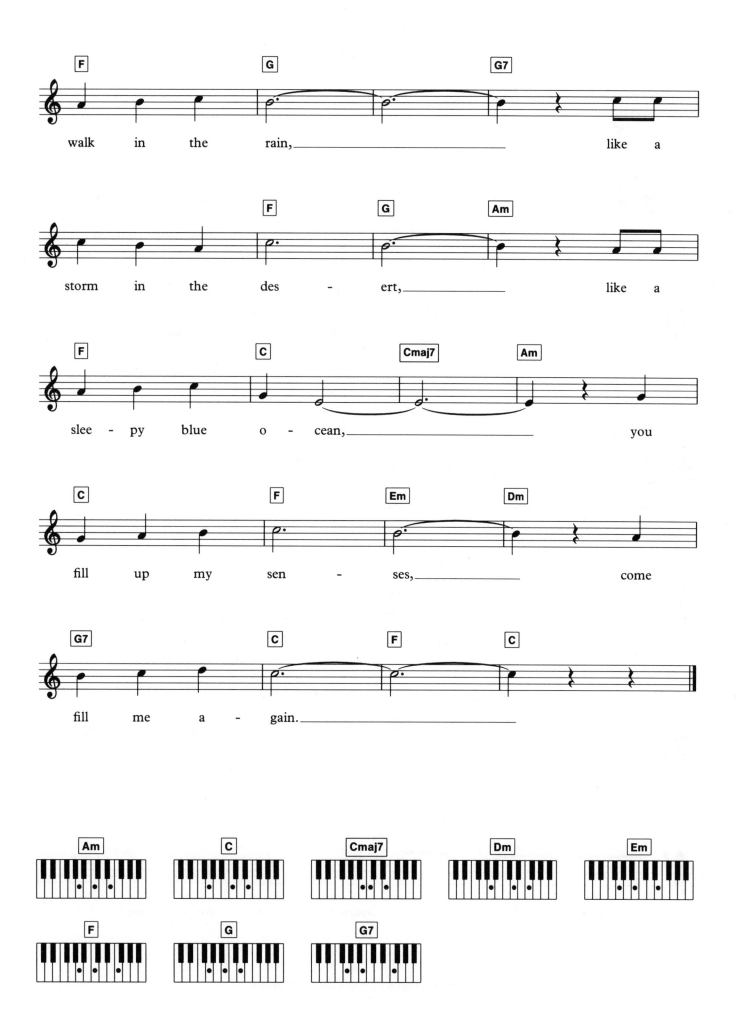

Bright Eyes

Words & Music by Mike Batt

Suggested Registration: Electric Piano
Rhythm: Soft Rock
Tempo: ♩ = 104

Is it a kind of __ dream, __ float - ing out on the

tide, _____ fol - low - ing the ri - ver of

death down - stream, oh, is it a dream?

There's a fog a - long __ the ho - ri - zon,

a strange glow in the sky, _____ and

no - bo - dy seems __ to know where you go,

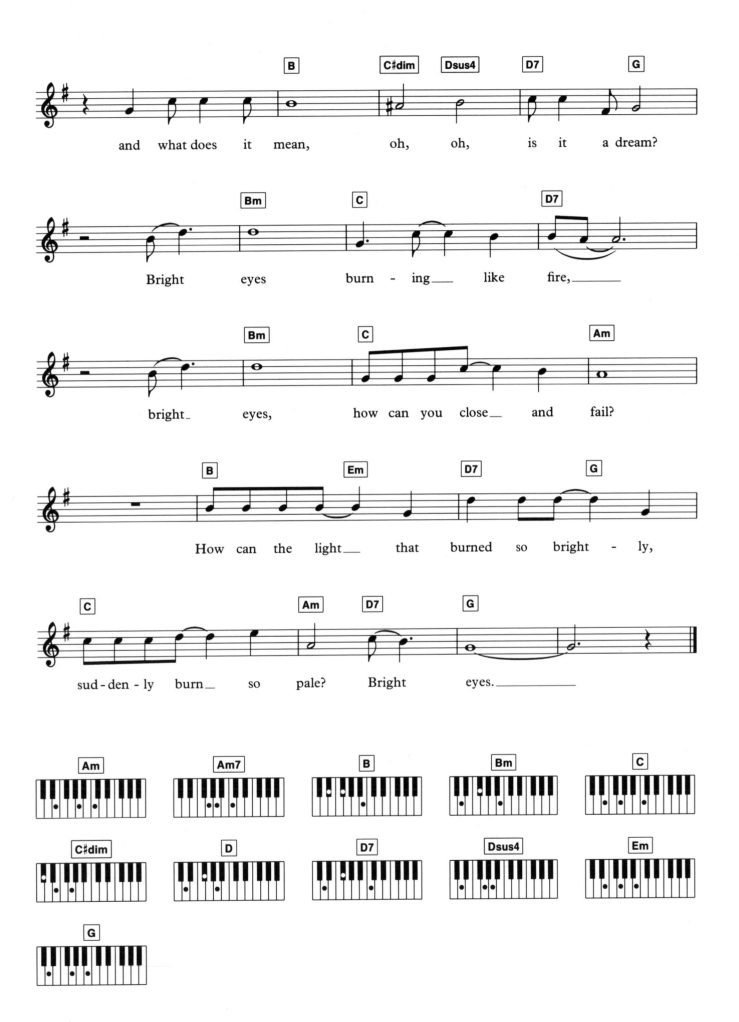

CONGRATULATIONS

Words & Music by Bill Martin and Phil Coulter

Suggested Registration: Clarinet
Rhythm: Swing
Tempo: ♩ = 180

Eternal Flame

Words & Music by Billy Steinberg, Tom Kelly and Susanna Hoffs

Suggested Registration: Acoustic Guitar
Rhythm: Pop Ballad / Soft Rock
Tempo: ♩ = 74

sun shines through the rain,___ a whole life so lone-ly, and then come and ease the pain.

I don't wan-na lose this feel - ing. Close your eyes,

give me your hand dar-ling. Do you feel my heart beat - ing? Do you un-der -

- stand? Do you feel the same?_ Am I on-ly dream-ing, or is this burn-ing

an e - ter-nal flame?_

FREEDOM

Words & Music by George Michael

Suggested Registration: Saxophone
Rhythm: Pop / 8 Beat
Tempo: ♩ = 132

Ev - ery day I hear a dif - ferent sto - ry,

peo - ple say-ing that you're no good for___ me, saw your lov - er with an -

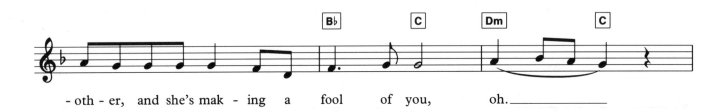

- oth - er, and she's mak - ing a fool of you, oh.___

If you loved me ba - by, you'd de - ny___ it, but you laugh and tell me

I should try___ it. Tell me I'm a ba - by, and I don't

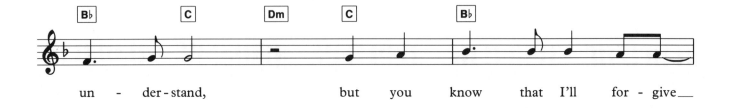

un - der - stand, but you know that I'll for - give___

GREAT BALLS OF FIRE

Words & Music by Jack Hammer and Otis Blackwell

Suggested Registration: Saxophone
Rhythm: Rock / Rock & Roll
Tempo: ♩ = 140

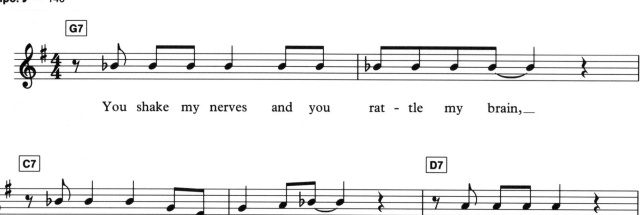

You shake my nerves and you rat - tle my brain,___

too much love drives a man in - sane,___ you broke my will,

but what a thrill, good - ness gra - cious, great___ balls of fi - re.

I laughed at love 'cause I thought it was fun - ny,

you came a - long and moved___ me hon - ey, I changed my mind,

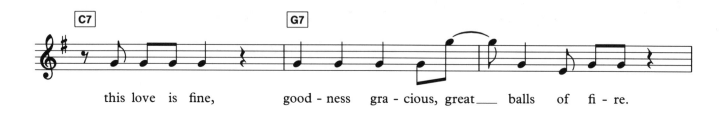

this love is fine, good - ness gra - cious, great___ balls of fi - re.

It's All In The Game

Words by Carl Sigman / Music by Charles G Dawes

Suggested Registration: Strings
Rhythm: Swing
Tempo: ♩ = 92

Ma - ny a tear has to fall, but it's all in the

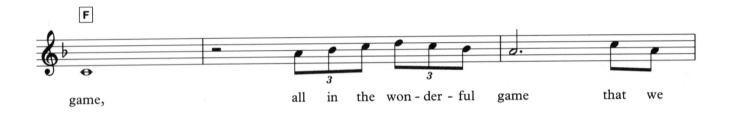

game, all in the won - der - ful game that we

know as love, you have words with

him, and your fu - ture's look - ing dim, but these

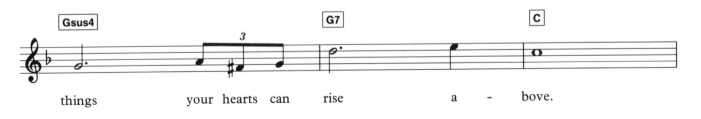

things your hearts can rise a - bove.

Once in a while he won't call, but it's all in the

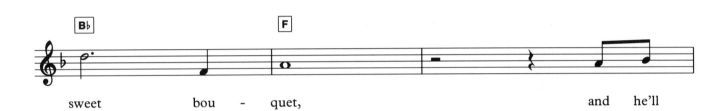

game, soon he'll be there at your side with a

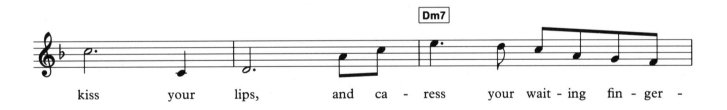

sweet bou - quet, and he'll

kiss your lips, and ca - ress your wait - ing fin - ger -

- tips, and your hearts will fly a - way._____

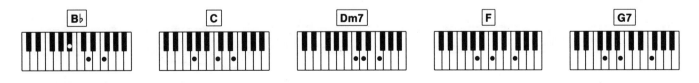

La Bamba

Arranged by Ritchie Valens

Suggested Registration: Piano
Rhythm: Cha-Cha-Cha
Tempo: ♩ = 134

-ne - ro,　　　yo no soy ma - ri - ne - ro, soy ca - pi - tan,__

__ soy ca - pi - tan, soy ca - pi - tan.____

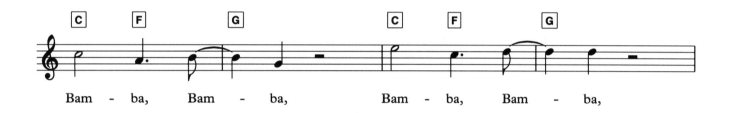

Bam - ba,　Bam - ba,　　Bam - ba,　Bam - ba,

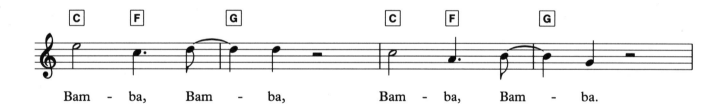

Bam - ba,　Bam - ba,　　Bam - ba,　Bam - ba.

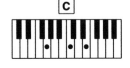
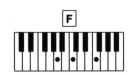
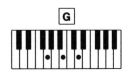

LIVING DOLL

Words & Music by Lionel Bart

Suggested Registration: Saxophone
Rhythm: Pop Swing
Tempo: ♩ = 112

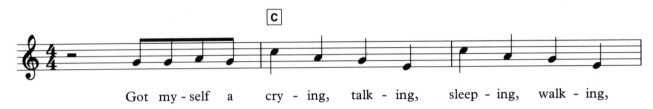

Got my-self a cry - ing, talk - ing, sleep - ing, walk - ing,

liv-ing doll, _ got to do my best to please her just 'cause she's a

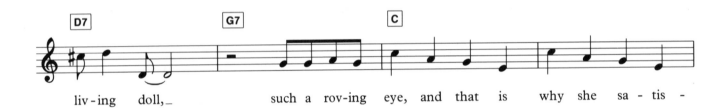

liv-ing doll, _ such a rov-ing eye, and that is why she sa - tis -

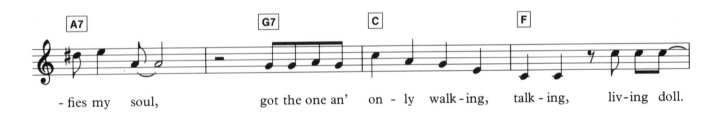

- fies my soul, got the one an' on - ly walk-ing, talk - ing, liv-ing doll.

_ Take a look at her hair, it's real, and if you don't be -

- lieve what I say, _ just feel, I'm gon - na lock her up in a trunk, so

MATCHSTALK MEN AND MATCHSTALK CATS AND DOGS

Words & Music by Michael Coleman and Brian Burke

Suggested Registration: Acoustic Guitar
Rhythm: Country
Tempo: ♩ = 136

He paint-ed Sal-ford's smo-key tops on card-board box-es from the shops, parts of An-coats where I used to play, I'm sure he once walked down our street, 'cause he paint-ed kids who had now't on their feet, the clothes they wore had all seen bet-ter days. And he paint-ed match-stalk men and

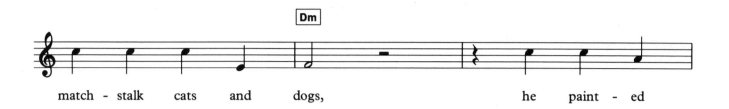

match - stalk   cats   and   dogs,   he   paint - ed

kids   on   the   cor - ner   of   the   street   that   were spark - ing   clogs,

now   he   takes   his   brush and   he   waits____   out -

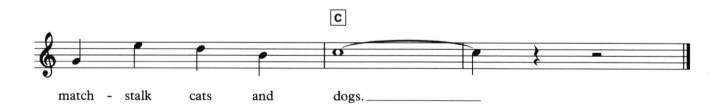

- side   them   fac - tory   gates,____   to   paint   his   match - stalk   men   and

match - stalk   cats   and   dogs._____

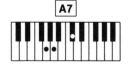

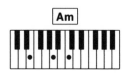

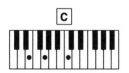

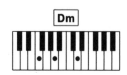

Moon River

Words by Johnny Mercer / Music by Henry Mancini

Suggested Registration: Strings
Rhythm: Slow Waltz
Tempo: ♩ = 82

Moon Ri - ver wi - der than a mile, I'm

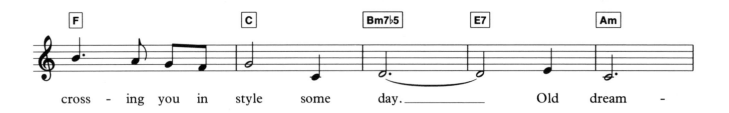

cross - ing you in style some day._____ Old dream -

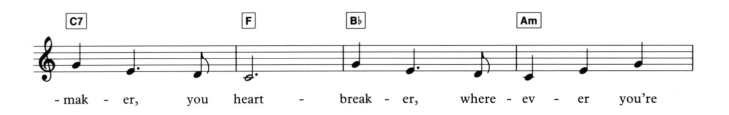

- mak - er, you heart - break - er, where - ev - er you're

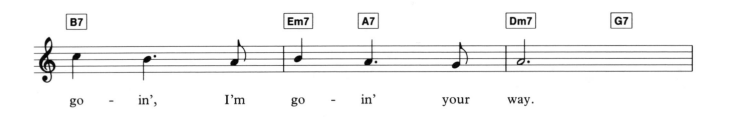

go - in', I'm go - in' your way.

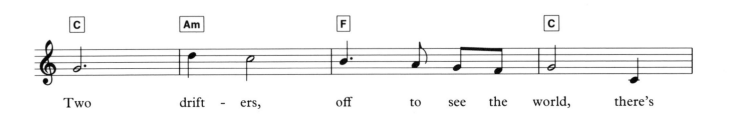

Two drift - ers, off to see the world, there's

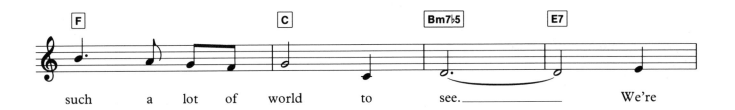

such a lot of world to see._____ We're

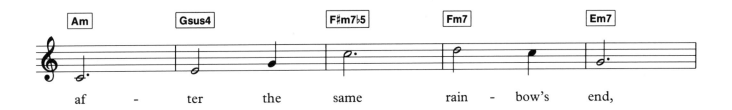

af - ter the same rain - bow's end,

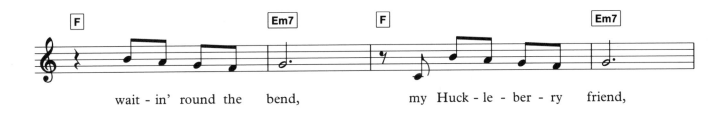

wait - in' round the bend, my Huck - le - ber - ry friend,

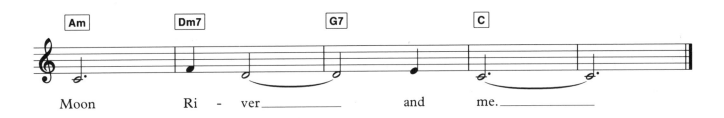

Moon Ri - ver_____ and me._____

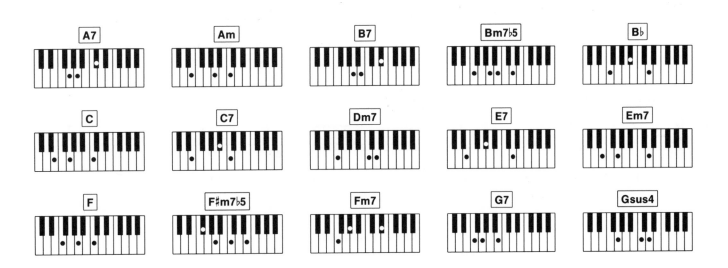

ONLY SIXTEEN

Words & Music by Barbara Campbell

Suggested Registration: Saxophone
Rhythm: Pop Swing
Tempo: ♩ = 124

Sealed With A Kiss

Words by Peter Udell / Music by Gary Geld

Suggested Registration: Flute
Rhythm: Soft Rock
Tempo: ♩ = 98

Seasons In The Sun
(Le Moribond)

Music and Original French Words by Jacques Brel / English Words by Rod McKuen

Suggested Registration: Horn
Rhythm: Soft Rock
Tempo: ♩ = 96

33

Stand By Me

Words & Music by Ben E King, Jerry Leiber and Mike Stoller

Suggested Registration: Saxophone
Rhythm: Soul / Pop
Tempo: ♩ = 108

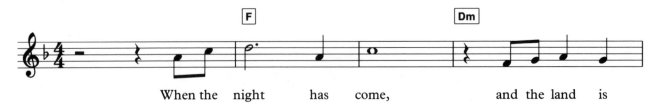

When the night has come, and the land is

dark, and the moon_____ is the on - ly_____ light we'll

see, no I won't be a -

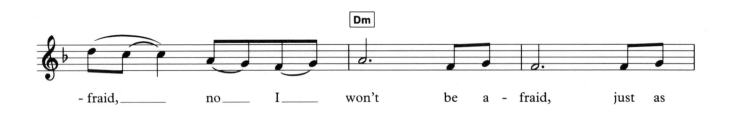

- fraid,_____ no_____ I_____ won't be a - fraid, just as

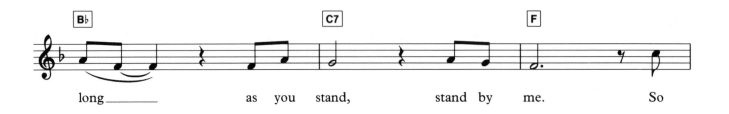

long_____ as you stand, stand by me. So

dar - ling, dar - ling, stand by me, oh,_____

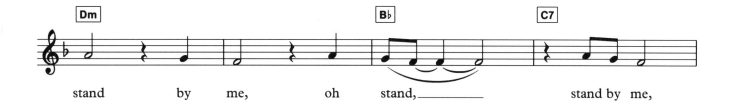

stand by me, oh stand,_____ stand by me,

stand by me. So dar - ling, dar - ling, stand by

me, oh,_____ stand by me, oh stand,_____

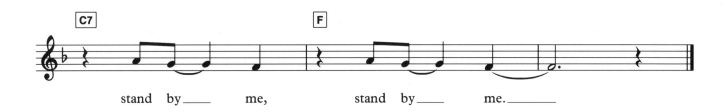

stand by____ me, stand by____ me._____

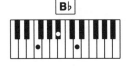
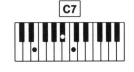
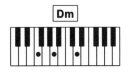
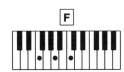

Summer Holiday

Words & Music by Bruce Welch and B Bennett

Suggested Registration: Vibraphone
Rhythm: Pop Swing
Tempo: ♩ = 108

We're all go - ing on a sum - mer ho - li - day,

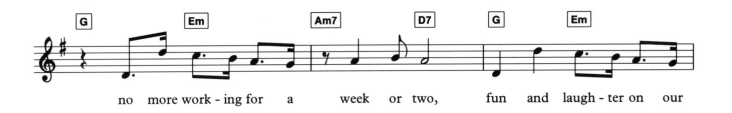

no more work - ing for a week or two, fun and laugh - ter on our

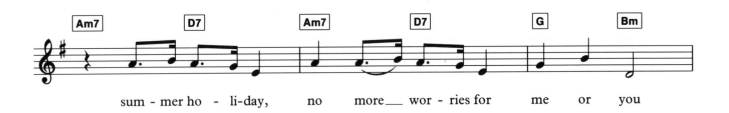

sum - mer ho - li - day, no more___ wor - ries for me or you

for a week___ or two. We're go - ing where the sun shines

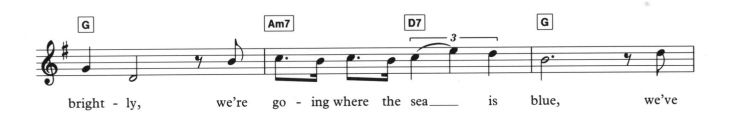

bright - ly, we're go - ing where the sea___ is blue, we've

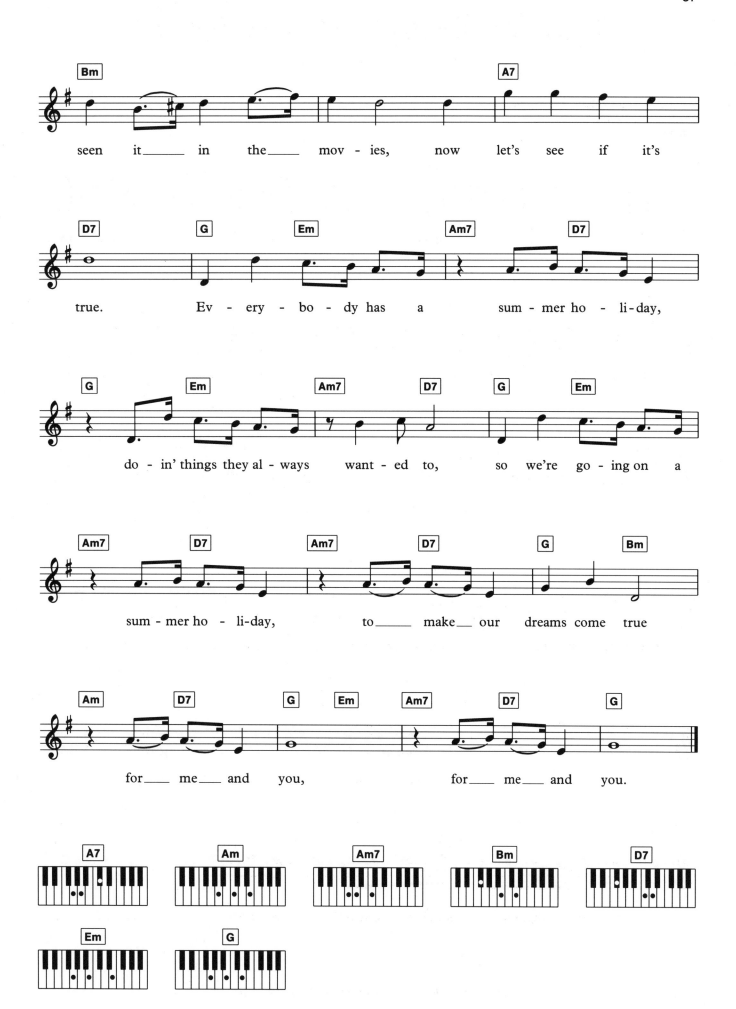

WAKE ME UP BEFORE YOU GO-GO

Words & Music by George Michael

Suggested Registration: Saxophone
Rhythm: Pop Swing
Tempo: ♩ = 132

You put the boom boom in-to my heart,___ you send my

soul sky high when your lov-ing starts, jit-ter-bug in-to my brain,

_____ goes a-bang bang bang till my feet do the same,_ if

some-thing's bug-ging you, if some-thing ain't_ right, my best friend told me what

you did last night left me seeth-ing in my bed,___

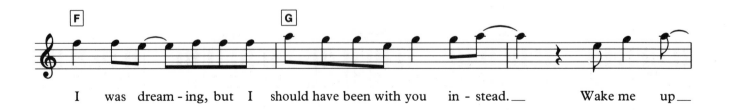

I was dream-ing, but I should have been with you in-stead.___ Wake me up___

_ be-fore you go,___ go, don't leave me hang - ing on___ like a yo -

- yo, wake me up___ be-fore you go,___ go, I don't wan-na miss_

_ it when you get that high,___ wake me up___ be - fore you go,_

_ go, 'cause I'm not plan - ning on___ go - ing so - lo, wake me up_

_ be-fore you go,___ go, take me danc - ing to - night._____

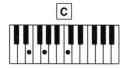
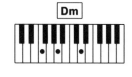
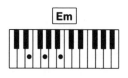
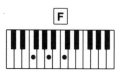
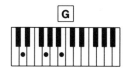

WHAT A WONDERFUL WORLD

Words & Music by George David Weiss and Bob Thiele

Suggested Registration: Vibraphone
Rhythm: Ballad
Tempo: ♩ = 76

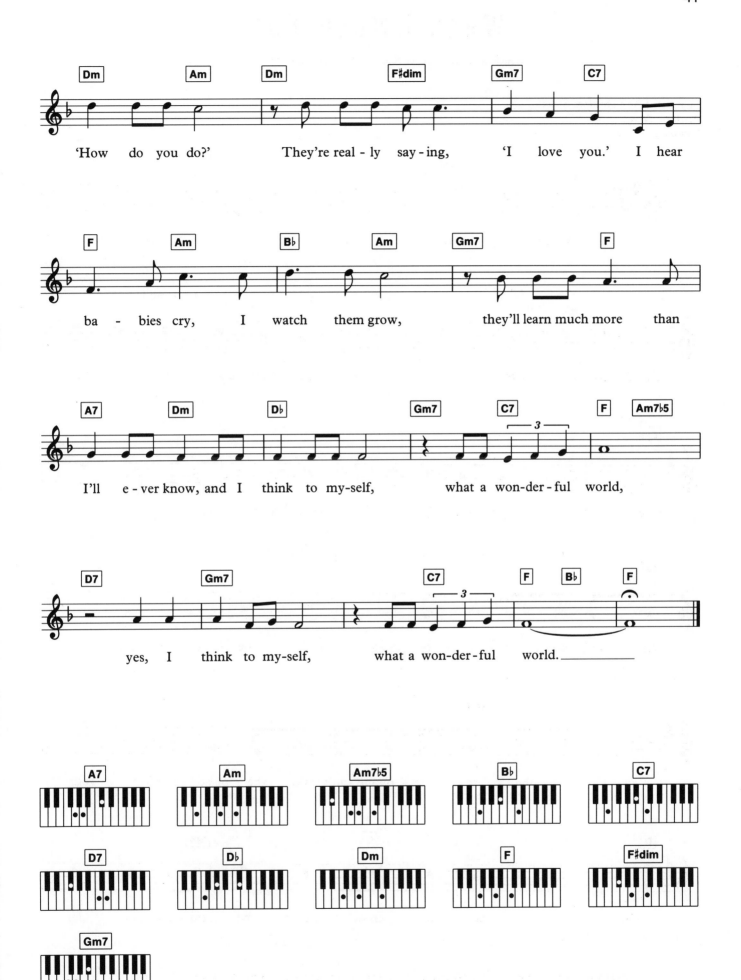

When I Need You

Words by Carole Bayer Sager / Music by Albert Hammond

Suggested Registration: Strings
Rhythm: Waltz
Tempo: ♩ = 132

A Whiter Shade Of Pale

Words & Music by Keith Reid and Gary Brooker

Suggested Registration: Pipe Organ
Rhythm: Soft Rock
Tempo: ♩ = 78

Without You

Words & Music by Pete Ham and Tom Evans

Suggested Registration: Piano
Rhythm: Soft Rock
Tempo: ♩ = 68

Well I can't for-get this eve - ning, or your

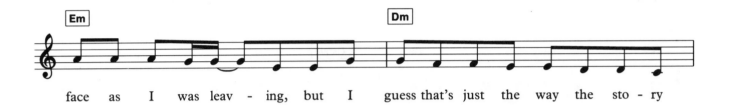

face as I was leav - ing, but I guess that's just the way the sto - ry

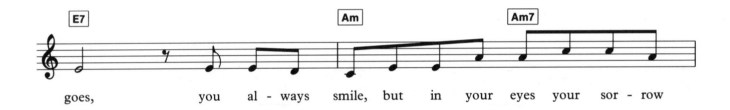

goes, you al - ways smile, but in your eyes your sor - row

shows, yes, it shows._____ No I

can't for-get to-mor - row, when I think of all my sor - row, when I

had you there, but then I let you go, and now it's

The Easy Keyboard Library Series

Big Band Hits Order Ref: 19098	**Popular Classics** Order Ref: 4180A
Blues Order Ref: 3477A	**Pub Singalong Collection** Order Ref: 3954A
Celebration Songs Order Ref: 3478A	**Rock 'n' Roll Classics** Order Ref: 2224A
Christmas Carols Order Ref: 4616A	**Traditional Scottish Favourites** Order Ref: 4231A
Christmas Songs Order Ref: 19198	**Showtunes - Volume 1** Order Ref: 19103
Classic Hits - Volume 1 Order Ref: 19099	**Showtunes - Volume 2** Order Ref: 3328A
Classic Hits - Volume 2 Order Ref: 19100	**Soft Rock Collection** Order Ref: 4617A
Country Songs Order Ref: 19101	**Soul Classics** Order Ref: 19201
Traditional English Favourites Order Ref: 4229A	**Summer Collection** Order Ref: 3489A
Favourite Hymns Order Ref: 4179A	**TV Themes** Order Ref: 19196
Film Classics Order Ref: 19197	**The Twenties** Order Ref: 2969A
Great Songwriters Order Ref: 2225A	**The Thirties** Order Ref: 2970A
Instrumental Classics Order Ref: 2338A	**The Forties** Order Ref: 2971A
Traditional Irish Favourites Order Ref: 4230A	**The Fifties** Order Ref: 2972A
Love Songs - Volume 1 Order Ref: 19102	**The Sixties** Order Ref: 2973A
Love Songs - Volume 2 Order Ref: 19199	**The Seventies** Order Ref: 2974A
Music Hall Order Ref: 3329A	**The Eighties** Order Ref: 2975A
Motown Classics Order Ref: 2337A	**The Nineties** Order Ref: 2976A
Number One Hits Order Ref: 19200	**Wartime Collection** Order Ref: 3955A

Wedding Collection
Order Ref: 3688A

Exclusive distributors:

International Music Publications Limited
Griffin House 161 Hammersmith Road, London W6 8BS
International Music Publications Limited
25 Rue D'Hauteville, 75010 Paris, France
International Music Publications GmbH Germany
Marstallstrasse 8, D-80539 München, Germany
Nuova Carisch S.R.L.
Via M.F. Quintiliano 40, 20138 Milano, Italy
Danmusik
Vognmagergade 7, DK-1120 Copenhagen K, Denmark

THE EASY KEYBOARD LIBRARY